Pie in the Sky
Lois Ehlert

SCHOLASTIC INC.

New York Toronto London Auckland Sydney
Mexico City New Delhi Hong Kong Buenos Aires

This tree
was here when
we moved in.

Dad showed me buds on our tree today. He says that's a good sign, but we won't know till summer if we'll get pie.

I see yellow leaves
with green spots,
brown buds,
a brown chrysalis,
and a gray snow sky.
But no pie.

Winter's finally over. Sweet spring is here at last. Buds we saw last fall are bursting into bloom.

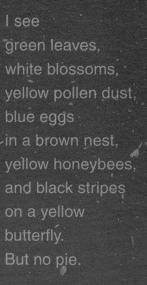

I see
green leaves,
white blossoms,
yellow pollen dust,
blue eggs
in a brown nest,
yellow honeybees,
and black stripes
on a yellow
butterfly.
But no pie.

But now a damp wind
is blowing, and all
the flower petals
are falling down
like rain.

I see
white petals,
dark gray tails,
brown branches,
and a gray rain sky.
But no pie.

You know what? I think something's finally growing on that tree of ours.

I see
orange and
lime green balls,
yellow moon and stars,
a pale green moth,
and a dark blue sky.
But no pie.

The birds sure
sound excited.
I wonder what's
going on.

I see
a robin's rusty red breast
and white-speckled throat,
a gray catbird with a
black crown and tail,
and purple-violet clouds
in a pink-and-orange sky.
But no pie.

Uh-oh.

Now
I see.

I see
brown cherry pits,
red wing tips
on cedar waxwings,
and white rings
around robins'
black eyes.
But no pies.

It's a
cherry
feast!

I see
orange-breasted
orioles,
black spots and tips
on butterfly wings,
red ripe cherries,
and a bright blue sky.
But no pie.

But, hey, raccoon,
save some
for us!

I see
a raccoon's black mask,
black toes,
black nose and eye,
and the
lime green glow
of fireflies.
But no pies.

At last
Dad says it's
time for *us*
to pick
cherries.

I see
gray wings,
a black-and-orange tail,
a yellow beak,
a silver gray pail,
and a blue fly.
Still no pie.

We're
going
to make
a pie!

First we wash
the cherries.

4 cups
sour
red
cherries

We squeeze out
all the
pits

and
save
the
juice.

Then we put the
cherries in a bowl.

½ cup juice

We add the juice,
flour, sugar, and
cinnamon,
and stir it with
a spoon.

5 tbsp. flour

1⅓
cups
sugar

½ tsp. cinnamon

Next we mix
the piecrust
dough.

We roll out two crusts
and press one
in the pan.

Then we pour the filling in.

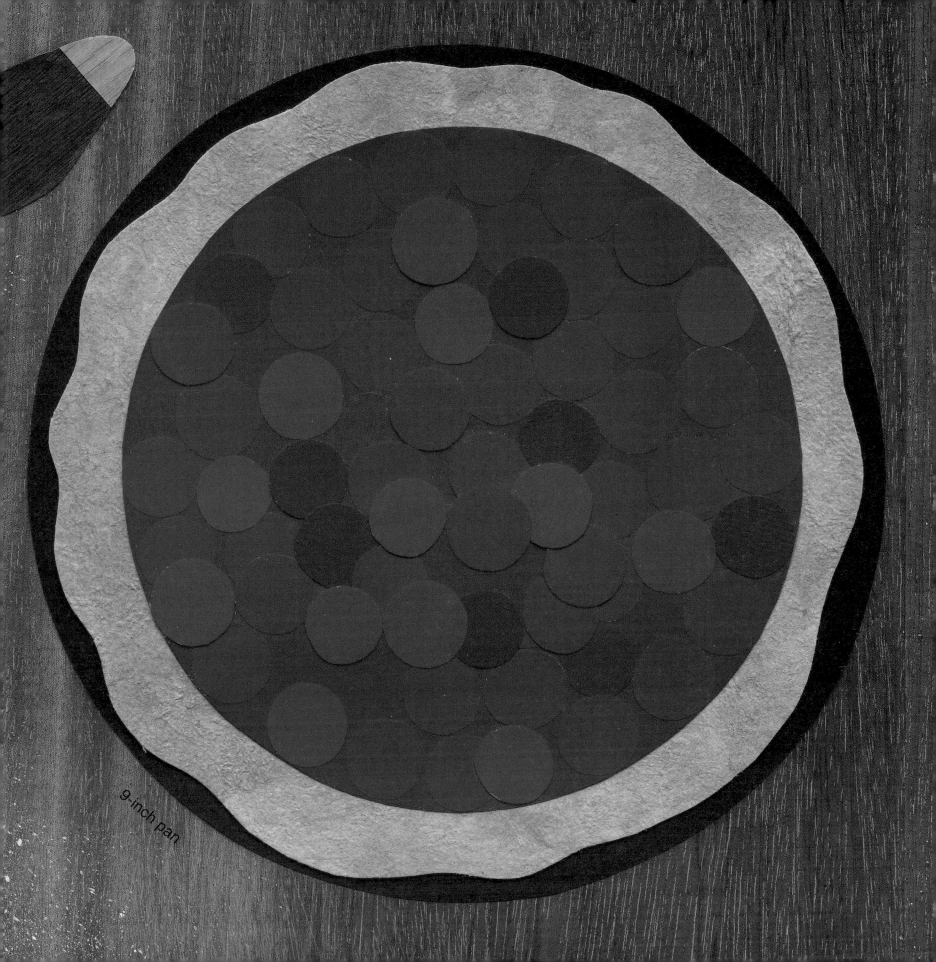

9-inch pan

We add
the top crust,
put the pie
in the oven,

and
wait
for it
to bake.

Press around crust edge with a fork to seal.

Cut design into crust so steam can escape while baking.

Preheat oven to 450°. Bake 10 minutes.

Reduce heat to 350°. Bake 35 to 45 minutes, until brown.

Now
Dad
cuts the pie.

He
puts
a piece
on each plate.

Wow!
That was
the best pie
I've ever
eaten.

I wonder if the
birds would like it?